Richard Scarry

L

Days of the Week
Months of the Year
Hours of the Day

CUBS

COLLINS COLOUR CUBS

The Days of the Week

SUNDAY   MONDAY   TUESDAY
WEDNESDAY   THURSDAY   FRIDAY
SATURDAY

At school, Miss Honey teaches many things. When she is not teaching, she is very busy doing other things.

On **Sunday** afternoon, she drove out into the country with her friend, Mr Bruno, to have a picnic. Picnics are always fun. Don't you think so?

On **Monday**, after school, she did a big wash.

On **Tuesday** morning, before school,
she baked a cake for the sick
children in the hospital.

Mother Cat took it to them.

On **Wednesday**, she made up packages of
used clothing to send to children
who do not have enough to wear.

On **Thursday**, she had a meeting with the
headmaster and the other teachers
to plan a school
picnic.

On **Friday**, she went to the library.
She is always learning new things to
teach the children.

On **Saturday**, she did her shopping.
And on Saturday night, she invited
Mr Bruno to dinner. He always
brings flowers when he visits her.
After dinner, he took Miss Honey to
the cinema.

You are a very busy lady, Miss Honey!

Janitor Joe and the Months of the Year

Joe is the school janitor.
A janitor takes care of the school
building. He fixes things when
they get broken. He works in the
school all the year round.

The first month of the year is
January.
January is sometimes a snowy month.
When it snows, Joe shovels a path
through the deep snow.

In **February**, he spreads sand on the icy pavement so that no one will slip.

What happened?
Did you slip, Joe?

In **March**, the strong winds blow.
Joe has trouble emptying the
waste-paper baskets.

In **April**, the rain falls from the sky and makes the plants grow.

Joe makes sure that the plants in the school garden get plenty of water.

The Easter Bunny comes in April.

In **May**, Joe mows the school lawn
with the lawnmower.
Once the mower got away and ran into
a supermarket.

Do you think it was tired of eating
nothing but grass?

In **June**, Miss Honey asked Joe to fix the classroom table. One leg wobbled a little bit.
Well, he really fixed it, didn't he?
You can fix it properly during the holidays, Joe.

We will see you when school starts again. Keep the school looking nice, Joe!

In **July**, when everyone was away on holiday, Joe gave everything a fresh coat of paint.

table

Huckle's chair

Lowly Worm's chair

Careful, Joe!

The month of **August** is hot and
sunny. That's when Joe fixed the
showers in the gym.
He pretended that he was at the
seaside.

In **September**, just before school
started, Joe made a new cement path
for the children to walk on.
It is still soft and wet. Tomorrow
it should be hard and dry.

Nice work, Joe!

I think you should have made it a few days sooner, Joe!

In **October**, the leaves begin to fall.
Joe raked them up and carried them
in his wheelbarrow to a big pile.
He burned them in an open place so
that nothing else would catch fire.

Do you see what I see?

November is a cold and windy month.
Winter is here.
Joe sawed the dead
branches off the trees
so that they wouldn't
be broken off by the
wind and fall on top of
something.
The headmaster came out
to look at his new car.

In **December**, there
are lots of holiday
celebrations.
Joe put up the
school Christmas
tree. He put on
the decorations.
It looks beautiful.
So far Joe has done
something right
for a change. He
has only to put the
star on the top.
Can you reach it.
Joe?

The Hours of the Day

It was Saturday. There was no school. But there were lots of things for Huckle to do. His friend, Lowly, had come to visit him. He had stayed overnight.

At **7** o'clock Huckle bounced out of bed.

At **8** o'clock he ate his breakfast.

Father Cat took the tablecloth with him to work.

At 9 o'clock he tidied his room.

At 10 o'clock he went to the shops.

At 11 o'clock he played in the garden with Lowly. He fell down a few times in a muddy puddle.

12 o'clock is midday. Huckle and
Lowly ate their lunches.
Lowly remembered to take his hat off
at table.

At 1 o'clock they both went for a nap.

At **2** o'clock they went for a drive.
They bumped into Joe, the school
janitor. He had been hurrying. He
was late for work again.

At **3** o'clock they walked home.

At **4** o'clock they watched
television.

At **5** o'clock
Father Cat came
home.

At 6 o'clock Mother Cat served supper.

She served Huckle's guest first.

It was a big surprise.
Father Cat is in for a big surprise, too.

At **7** o'clock Father Cat
gave Huckle and Lowly
their baths.
"Where did that soap go?"
asked Father Cat.

At **8** o'clock Father Cat read them
a bedtime story in bed.

And at 9 o'clock they
were sound asleep.

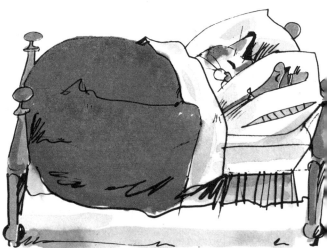

Sleep tight, Huckle!
Sleep tight, Lowly!

ISBN 0 00 123516 8
Printed in Great Britain